Harry Potter™

CELEBRATORY

EDITION

★ ★ ★

*The Best of
Harry Potter Colouring*

**STUDIO
PRESS**

An Insight Editions Book

*F*rom the orange, brown, and green hues used to convey the warmth and whimsy of the Weasley family to the emerald green and silver of Slytherin house, colour was an essential element in bringing Harry Potter to life on-screen and achieving an atmosphere full of enchantment.

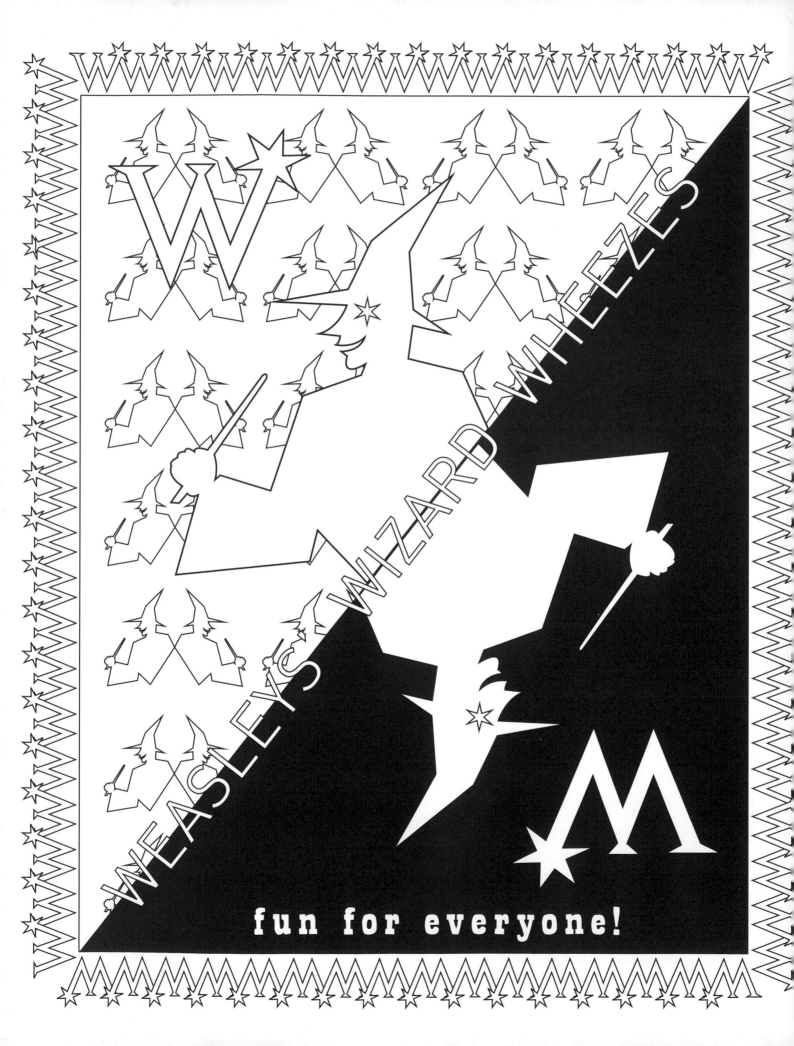

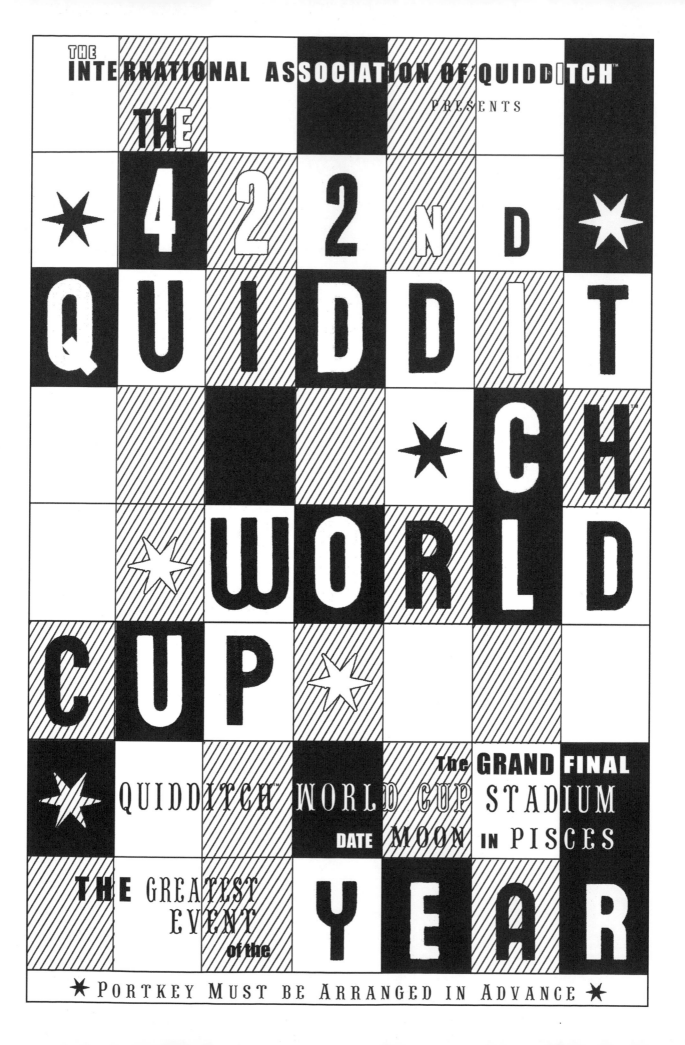

THE CREATURES AND BEASTS

of the wizarding world are majestic and funny, chilling and loving. They are as diverse a group of characters as the students who attend Hogwarts School of Witchcraft and Wizardry, and just as much a part of the magic of the Harry Potter films. The pages that follow present a selection of the fauna from the films and invite you to reimagine the fiery red feathers of Fawkes, the ghostly hues of the merpeople, the weathered scales of dragons – and so much more.

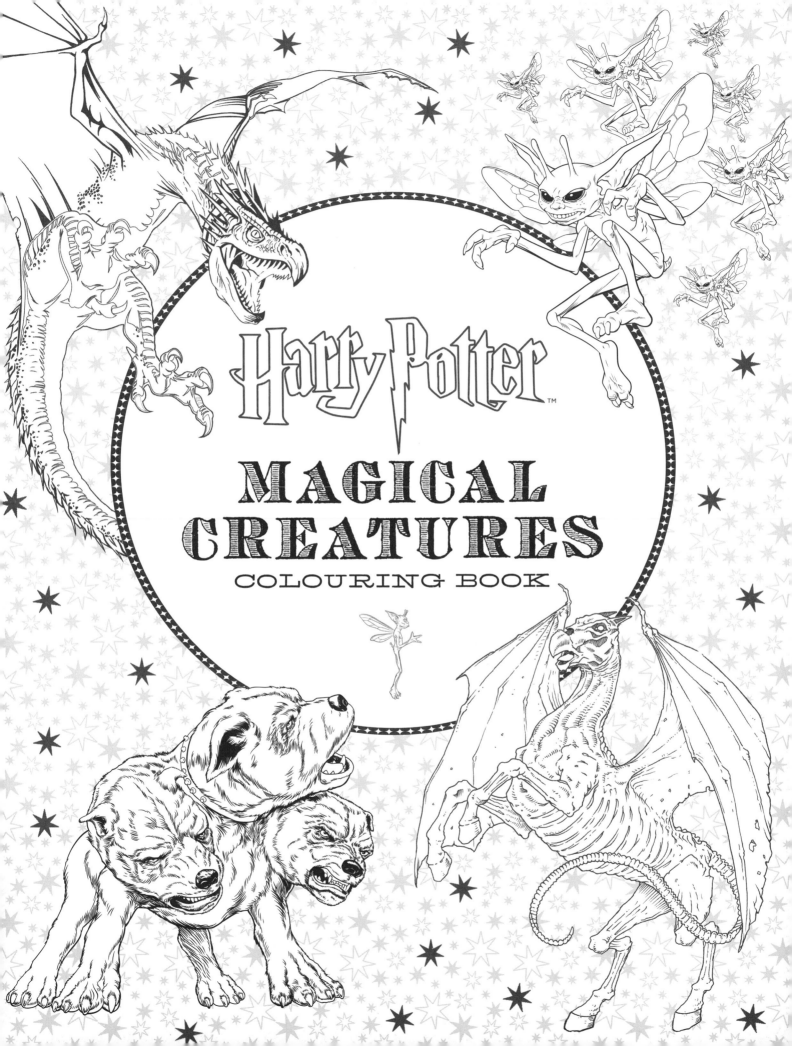

The world we journey through in the Harry Potter films is magical and extraordinary. From a bank run by goblins to a castle filled with staircases that move, we are continually taken to new and incredible places. We follow a young boy who has discovered a world he never knew existed and we encounter there a thrilling cast of wizards, witches and so much more. The pages that follow are an invitation to relive the magic of the Harry Potter films and bring your own vibrant colours to the wizarding world outlined here in black and white.

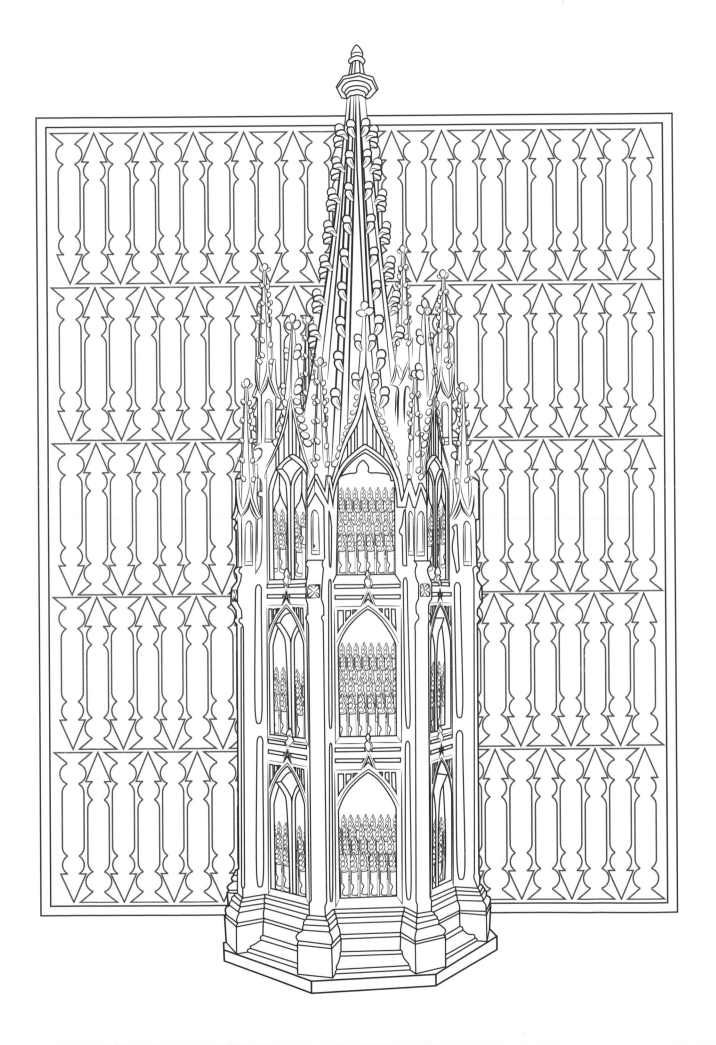